Mom's Secret

Meredith Costain ● illustrated by Janet Wolf

Copyright © Scholastic Australia Pty Limited, 1997.
All rights reserved. Published by Scholastic Inc.
READING DISCOVERY is a trademark of Scholastic Inc.
First published in 1997 by Scholastic Australia Pty Limited.
Printed in Hong Kong.
ISBN 0-590-76998-7.
Designed by Jobi Murphy.

25 24 23　　　　　　　　08　　　　　　　　14 15/0

SCHOLASTIC INC.

New York　Toronto　London　Auckland　Sydney

My mom has a secret.
Every day I ask her what it is,
but she won't tell me.
"It's a secret," she says. "But you can
try to guess it. Ask me questions."

"Is it something I can play with?" I ask.

"Yes," says Mom. "Ask me another question."

"Is it something I will love?" I ask. "Yes," says Mom. "Ask me another question."

"Is it something I can show my friends?" I ask.

"Yes," says Mom.

"Ask me another question."

"Is it something for everyone
in the family?" I ask.

"Yes," says Mom. She pats her tummy
and smiles.

"Guess what it is."

"A new puppy?" I ask.

Mom shakes her head and laughs.

"I'm going to have a baby," says Mom.

A baby!

"Will it be a boy or a girl?" I ask.

"That's the baby's secret!" says Mom.